Garfield

The Great Lover

JIM DAVIS

RR

RAVETTE BOOKS

First published by Ravette Books Limited 1982
Reprinted 1983, 1984, 1985, 1986, 1987
This edition first published 1988
Reprinted 1989, 1990, 1991, 1992

Printed and bound in Great Britain
for Ravette Books Limited,
3 Glenside Estate, Star Road, Partridge Green,
Horsham, West Sussex RH13 8RA
An Egmont Company
by Cox & Wyman Ltd, Reading

ISBN 0 906710 06 5

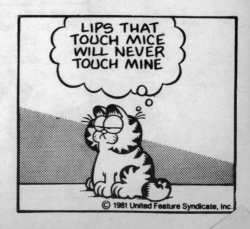

© 1981 United Feature Syndicate, Inc.

© 1981 United Feature Syndicate, Inc.

BAP!

© 1982 United Feature Syndicate Inc

© 1982 United Feature Syndicate, Inc.

© 1982 United Feature Syndicate Inc

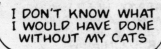

© 1982 United Feature Syndicate, Inc

1-20

JIM DAVIS

© 1982 United Feature Syndicate Inc

9-29

© 1981 United Feature Syndicate, Inc.

10-3

© 1981 United Feature Syndicate, Inc.

9-11

© 1981 United Feature Syndicate, Inc.

© 1981 United Feature Syndicate, Inc.

ROWRR!!

JIM DAVIS 6-25

© 1981 United Feature Syndicate, Inc.

YOU WAIT HERE WHILE I GO INTO THE STORE

JIM DAVIS

LEASHES ARE THE GREATEST THINGS SINCE SLICED BREAD

6-26

BY THE WAY, DON'T FORGET THE FROZEN LASAGNA

OH, GARFIELD

© 1981 United Feature Syndicate, Inc.

BARK!

PETS

© 1981 United Feature Syndicate, Inc.

JIM DAVIS

5-6

© 1981 United Feature Syndicate, Inc.

JIM DAVIS

BARK!

4-14

12-14

© 1981 United Feature Syndicate, Inc.

TELL ME, DOC, IF WE WERE MARRIED,

WOULD YOU BE MRS. JON ARBUCKLE, OR DOCTOR MRS. JON ARBUCKLE, OR MRS. DOCTOR LIZ ARBUCKLE, OR...

JIM DAVIS

12-15   © 1981 United Feature Syndicate, Inc.

I HATE TO SEE A GROWN DOCTOR CRY

CLAIRE, BABY! WHAT SAY YOU AND I GO OUT TONIGHT AND PAINT THE TOWN RED, SWEETS?

JIM DAVIS   6-16

YEH, MAYBE ANOTHER TIME?

NOW WHO SHOULD I CALL?

TRY CLODS ANONYMOUS

© 1981 United Feature Syndicate, Inc.

© 1981 United Feature Syndicate, Inc.

© 1981 United Feature Syndicate, Inc.

© 1981 United Feature Syndicate, Inc

© 1981 United Feature Syndicate, Inc.   8-29

© 1981 United Feature Syndicate, Inc.

© 1981 United Feature Syndicate, Inc.

© 1980 United Feature Syndicate, Inc.

© 1981 United Feature Syndicate, Inc.

12-8

OTHER GARFIELD BOOKS IN THIS SERIES

No.	2	Garfield Why Do You Hate Mondays?	£2.50
No.	3	Garfield Does Pooky Need You?	£2.50
No.	4	Garfield Admit It, Odie's OK!	£2.50
No.	5	Garfield Two's Company	£2.50
No.	6	Garfield What's Cooking?	£2.50
No.	7	Garfield Who's Talking?	£2.50
No.	8	Garfield Strikes Again	£2.50
No.	9	Garfield Here's Looking At You	£2.50
No.	10	Garfield We Love You Too	£2.50
No.	11	Garfield Here We Go Again	£2.50
No.	12	Garfield Life and Lasagne	£2.50
No.	13	Garfield In The Pink	£2.50
No.	14	Garfield Just Good Friends	£2.50
No.	15	Garfield Plays It Again	£2.50
No.	16	Garfield Flying High	£2.50
No.	17	Garfield On Top Of The World	£2.50
No.	18	Garfield Happy Landings	£2.50
No.	19	Garfield Going Places	£2.50
No.	20	Garfield Le Magnifique!	£2.50
No.	21	Garfield In The Fast Lane	£2.50
No.	22	Garfield In Tune	£2.50
No.	23	Garfield The Reluctant Romeo	£2.50
No.	24	Garfield With Love From Me To You	£2.50

LANDSCAPE SERIES

Garfield The All-Round Sports Star	£2.95
Garfield The Irresistible	£2.95
Garfield On Vacation	£2.95
Garfield Weighs In!	£2.95
Garfield The Incurable Romantic	£2.95
Garfield Wraps It Up	£2.95
Garfield Rebel Without A Clue!	£2.95

COLOUR TREASURIES

The Second Garfield Treasury	£5.95
The Third Garfield Treasury	£5.95
The Fourth Garfield Treasury	£5.95
The Fifth Garfield Treasury	£5.95

COLOUR TV SPECIALS

Here Comes Garfield	£2.95
Garfield On The Town	£2.95
Garfield In The Rough	£2.95
Garfield In Disguise	£2.95
Garfield In Paradise	£2.95
Garfield Goes To Hollywood	£2.95
A Garfield Christmas	£2.95
Garfield's Thanksgiving	£2.95
Garfield's Feline Fantasies	£2.95
Garfield Gets A Life	£2.95
Garfield A Weekend Away	£4.95
Garfield Book Of Cat Names	£2.50
Garfield Best Ever	£4.95
Garfield The Easter Bunny?	£3.95
Garfield How To Party	£3.95
Garfield Selection	£5.95
Garfield His 9 Lives	£5.95
Garfield Diet Book	£4.95
Garfield Exercise Book	£4.95
Garfield Book Of Love	£5.95

All these books are available at your local bookshop or newsagent, or can be ordered direct from the publisher. Just tick the titles you require and fill in the form below. Prices and availability subject to change without notice.

Ravette Books Limited, 3 Glenside Estate, Star Road, Partridge Green, Horsham, West Sussex RH13 8RA.

Please send a cheque or postal order and allow the following for postage and packing. UK: Pocket-books—45p for one book, 20p for a second book and 15p for each additional book. Landscape Series – 50p for one book plus 30p for each additional book. TV Specials and Cat Names – 45p for one book plus 30p for each additional book. Other titles – 85p for one book plus 50p for each additional book ordered.

Name ....

Address ....

....